GOD LOVES YOU

2003

HEAVEN AND MIRTH®

Paul

God's Message Sent Apostle Post

AND
OTHER BIBLE STORIES TO TICKLE YOUR SOUL

by Mike Thaler

Illustrated by Dennis Adler

*Equiping Kids
for Life*

A Faith Parenting Guide can be found on page 32.

Dedicated to
Pastor Bill Jastram,
to teach with love.
Mike

Faith Kids™ is an imprint of
Cook Communications, Colorado Springs, Colorado 80918
Cook Communications, Paris, Ontario
Kingsway Communications, Eastbourne, England

PAUL: GOD'S MESSAGE SENT APOSTLE POST
© 2000 by Mike Thaler for text and Dennis Adler for illustrations

Published in association with the literary agency of Alive Communications, Inc.,
1465 Kelly Johnson Blvd., Suite 320, Colorado Springs CO 80920.

Edited by Jeannie Harmon
Design by Clyde Van Cleve

First hardcover printing, 2000
Printed in the Singapore
04 03 02 01 00   5 4 3 2 1

Library of Congress Cataloging-in-Publication Data
Thaler, Mike, 1936-
        Paul, God's message sent apostle post, and other Bible stories to tickle
your soul/by Mike Thaler; illustrated by Dennis Adler.
        p. cm. -- (Heaven and Mirth)
        Summary: Five stories, written in a humorous vein, based on incidents
taken from the book of Acts in the New Testament and focusing on the
importance of being honest.
        ISBN 0-7814-3433-5
        1. Bible stories, English—N.T. Acts. 2. Bible N.T. Acts—Juvenile humor.
[1. Bible. N.T.—Wit and humor. 2. Bible stories.—N.T.] I. Adler, Dennis
(Dennis H.), 1942- ill. II. Title.
BS2401.T45 2000
226.6'09505—dc21
                                                                00-023760

Letter from the Author

Taking this opportunity, I would like to share with you how this book came about. Born sixty-two years ago, I have been a secular children's book author most of my life. I was also content to have a fast-food relationship with God from the drive-by window. At the age of sixty, I came into the banquet by inviting Jesus Christ into my heart. Since then my life has been a glorious feast. These stories are part of that celebration.

One night I sat and watched a sincere grandfather trying to read Bible stories to his squirming grandchildren. I asked him, "Aren't there any humorous retellings of Bible stories that are vivid and alive for kids?" He rolled his eyes and said, "This is it." The kids rolled their eyes, too.

This made me sad, for the Bible is the most exciting, valuable, and alive book I know—as is its Author. So I went into my room, with this in mind, and wrote "Noah's Rainbow."

Since then God has anointed me with sixty stories that fire my imagination and light up my heart. They are stories which, I hope, are filled with the joy, love, and spirit of the Lord.

Mike Thaler
West Linn 1998

Nuggets from Goldie the miner prophet:
"It's Never Too Late to Eat Right."

Author's Note

I have conscientiously tried to follow each story in word and spirit as found in the Bible. But in some cases, for the sake of storytelling, I have taken minor liberties and added small details. I pray for your understanding in these instances.

3

4

The Day of Pentecost
That's Easy for You to Say

WHEN THE DAY OF PENTECOST ARRIVED,
many disciples were together in Jerusalem,
sitting around shooting the breeze.
Suddenly, each heard what sounded like a violent wind.
They all looked at each other as tongues of fire
descended from heaven and came to rest on them.

The Holy Spirit filled the room
and each disciple began speaking
a foreign language.

"This is better than Berlitz," said Peter.

Jerusalem was filled with Jews
from all over the world,
and a crowd quickly gathered
as they heard someone call to them
in their own language.
Parthians, Medes, Egyptians,
Cretans, and New Yorkers,
all heard the word of God
in their own accent.

"It's a regular U.N.!"
they all exclaimed.

"It's tongues in cheeks remarks,
so to speak."

"It's better than subtitles."

"The're just drunk,"
said some cynics.

"Hey," said Peter,
"It's only 9 AM.
We're not drunk on wine,
we're high on God.
It's just like the Prophet Joel said:

*"'I will pour out My Spirit
on all the people
and the world will be filled
with miracles, signs,
and wonders.'*

"Jesus came to you
direct from God
and performed those miracles,
signs, and wonders," Peter continued.

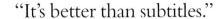

"You didn't take Him seriously.
No hard feelings.

"Then you put Him to death.
It's OK. Nobody's perfect.
But God raised Him
to live forever.

"As David said, *I told you so.*'

"Therefore, let all Israel know
that Christ, whom you
crucified, is the Savior
and Messiah sent by God."

"What can we do now?"
they all cried.

"Well, for starters,
you can say you're sorry
and be baptized,

and ask Jesus for forgiveness.
Then perhaps *you* will be
filled with the Holy Spirit."

"Will we get a second language?"

"More important than that," said Peter,
"you'll get a second chance for eternal life."

"Now you're talkin' our language,"
they all said, "We'll sign up."

And that day,
3,000 became believers.

THE END

Nuggets from Goldie the miner prophet
"Your Father's tongue is more important than your mother tongue."

For the real story, read Acts 2:1–41

9

Ananias and Sapphira
Early Retirement

ALL THE EARLY BELIEVERS were one in heart and mind. They shared everything, except toothbrushes. If one sold his house or his fields, he brought the proceeds to be divided among everyone.

Now when Ananias
and his wife, Sapphira,
unloaded their parcel,
they hid a portion of it away
for their early retirement,
sort of an IRA account.
Then Ananias laid
what was left at the feet
of the apostles.

Peter counted the money.
"Fifteen bucks! Boy, Ananias,
you gave away
a good piece of land for a song."

"Yeah," said Ananias,
"It's a buyer's market."

"You sure this is all you got?"

"May I drop dead if it isn't."
And he dropped dead.

When his wife came by
three hours later,
Paul said, "Are you sure
this is all you got for the land?"

"That's it, cross my heart
and hope to die."

Then she dropped dead too,
and was buried next to her husband.

When the story got around
to all the church members,
it made fundraising a lot easier.
And the joke went around,
"They put away a little
for early retirement,
so God retired them early."★

★This is a good example of
early church humor.

THE END

Nuggets from Goldie the miner prophet:
"God can be tougher than the I.R.S.!"

For the real story, read Acts 5:1–11.

Simon the Sorcerer
The Trick's Up

T<small>HERE WAS A SORCERER IN</small> S<small>AMARIA</small>★
named *Simon the Great.* He was a pretty good magician.
He could pull a camel out of a hat (a big hat),
saw a lady in half (a little lady),
and make your money disappear.
He had lots of tricks, and people were really impressed.
They started calling him *Simon the Divine,*
and worshiping him.

★Pronounced Some-Area

That was until they heard Philip
preaching the Gospel of Jesus,
and they all became baptized.

Even Simon himself became baptized,
and followed Philip everywhere
when he saw the signs and miracles
that God performed.

"This is quite an act," thought Simon.

And when Peter and John arrived
and everyone received the Holy Spirit,
Simon was *really* impressed.

"Hey guys," he said,
"could you teach me that trick?
I could headline in Vegas
with that one.
I'll even pay you for it."

"You are a real jerk," sighed Peter.
"You can't buy God's love or His gifts."

"Hey," said Simon, "Don't get so uptight.
Just teach me how to heal the blind;
I'll open a clinic."

"Forget it," said Peter,
and he and John
returned to Jerusalem,
preaching the Gospel
all the way.

Simon gave up show biz and
opened a trick shop
that sold exploding cigars,
hand buzzers,
and whoopee cushions.
He called it
"Pranks to God"!

THE END

Nuggets from Goldie the miner prophet:
"You can trick yourself, but you can't trick God."

For the real story, read Acts 8:9–25.

18

Peter and Cornelius
Something Ain't Kosher

WHILE **PETER** WAS WAITING FOR LUNCH,
he fell asleep on the roof.
Since he was hungry
he had a food dream.
God unrolled a big picnic
from heaven.

"So eat!" said God.

But when Peter took a
closer look at all the dishes,
he was appalled!

There was pork stroganoff,
sweet and sour clams,
and bacon foo yung.

"So eat already,"
said God.

"But, Lord,
this is a *pignic*,
a nonkosher buffet,
unclean cuisine."

**"Peter, everything
from My kitchen is edible."**

Peter woke up with a
queasy feeling in his stomach.
He was thinking about God's menu
when three men knocked at his door.

"Answer the door," said God.

"We're from Cornelius
the centurion,
a God-fearing man.
An angel told him to
invite you to dinner."

"Hey," said Peter,
"I haven't had lunch yet.
Come on in and have a knish.★"

The next day Peter went to see
Cornelius. He was having
a family reunion.

"Can you stay for dinner?"
asked Cornelius.

"Listen, I'm not even
supposed to be here.
But God is pushing me!"

★a Jewish tamale.

"God's pushing me too,"
said Cornelius.
   "Three days ago an angel
in a shiny suit told me
to invite you over."

   "I see now," exclaimed Peter,
"that God loves everyone
and everyone can love God."

   "You got it!" thundered God,
as the Holy Spirit fell upon everyone
in the house.

   "Wow!" said Peter
and he baptized the whole group
in the punch bowl.

   "Thank you," said Cornelius, drying off.
"Is there anything we can do for you?"

"I'm really hungry," said Peter, "When're we going to eat?"

"Now," smiled Cornelius. And they all sat down and had pork ribs, chitlins, and black-eyed peas.

THE END

Nuggets from Goldie the miner prophet:
"What you put in your heart is more important than what you put in your mouth."

For the real story, read Acts 10:1–48.

Paul in a Squall
God's Message Sent Apostle Post

I<small>F</small> P<small>AUL</small> <small>HAD COOLED IT IN COURT</small>,
King Agrippa would have set him free.
But he insisted on bringing his case before Caesar,
so he found himself on the way to Rome
in the custody of a centurion named Julius.

After sailing around
for a while,
they landed
in a harbor
called Fair Havens.
It was getting
close to
the hurricane season,
so Paul warned Julius
that if they sailed on
it would be a disaster.

But Julius listened to the travel agent
who booked them on the *Titanicus*.

"Big mistake!" said Paul as he got on board.

And sure enough,
after two days of smooth sailing, a hurricane hit.

The ship was tossed *to and fro,*
four and fro,
  eight and fro, . . .
    it was a bad storm.

  "I told ya so," said Paul.

  The sailors threw all the
    FedEx packages overboard,
    since they couldn't make
    their two-day delivery
    anyway, and wouldn't
      eat a bite.

      "Come on, boys," said Paul,
        "How about a little
          pepperoni pizza?"

      Everyone threw up.

Then the waves threw up walls of water
and spun the boat like a feather
in a washing machine.

"Stay cool," shouted Paul
above the storm,
"God has guaranteed our safety."

After fourteen days
of spinning,
the captain
and the crew
decided
to abandon ship.
But Paul and the
Roman soldiers
prevented them.

"Stick with us, guys.
I've just made a big
batch of lasagna,
so help yourselves."
They all threw up again.

Then on the morning
of the fifteenth day, they spotted
some beach umbrellas,
a condominium,
and a restaurant.

"We're saved!" they all shouted.

But before they could
make it to the *salad bar*,
they struck a *sandbar*
and sunk.
The Roman soldiers
wanted to kill Paul,
but Julius saved him,
and they swam ashore.
They arrived just in time
for a barbecue.

The evening was almost ruined
when Paul was bitten
by a deadly snake
hiding in a hot dog bun.
Everyone expected him to die.
When he didn't . . .
the party went on.

In fact, Paul cured
everyone on the island
from heatstroke,
to heartstroke
and they all said
he must be a god.

"No," smiled Paul,
"I'm not. I just work
for Him.

THE END

Nuggets from Goldie the miner prophet.
"No matter how rough it gets, you won't sink if God is your skipper."

For the real story, read Acts 27:1 – 28:10.

HEAVEN AND MIRTH®

Paul

God's Message Sent Apostle Post

Age: 6 and up

Life Issue: Learning to be honest with God
and other people is important.

Spiritual Building Block: Honesty

Learning Styles

Help your child learn about honesty in the following ways:

Sight: View a story video or read stories from a Bible storybook that recount times when people were honest or dishonest. Achan, Ananias and Sapphira, and Queen Esther are some examples. What happened to people that were dishonest with God? Does God honor honesty?

Sound: Share with your child some examples of times in your life when you had an opportunity to be honest or dishonest. What decision did you make and why? What happened as a result of your decision? Sometimes we learn by the mistakes we make and then have to pay the consequences. God desires that we be truthful and honest both with Him and with other people.

Touch: Take several items that your child values (a favorite toy or book, a food item, a favorite video, etc.). Place a monetary value on each item. Get some money from your wallet and give it to your child to take to your make-believe store. Have your child purchase the items with the money, but create situations where the child either gets too much or too little money back. Ask: How do you feel when people have not been honest with you? How do you feel when you know that you haven't been honest? What does God expect of us. Talk to your child about the importance of each party being fair and honest.